Phonics Reading Program 2

Book 7
long o

Where Is Our Boat?

by Quinlan B. Lee

SCHOLASTIC INC.

New York Toronto London Auckland Sydney
Mexico City New Delhi Hong Kong Buenos Aires

We are on a **boat.**
Do you know where we are?

Look at our big **coats.**
They keep us as warm as
toast.

What can **float** in the water?
Ice!
Ice can **float.**

Who is on the ice **float**? Their fur **coats** keep them as warm as **toast**.

Look!
Is that an ice **float**?
Is it a **boat**?
No. What is it?

Look at the **coast.**
Who is that?
They love to swim and
float.

Big **coats.**
Seals on ice **floats.**
Whales as big as **boats.**
Penguins on the **coast.**

Right! We are at the South Pole.